nickelodeon™

SpongeBob SquarePants™

This annual belongs to

....

Contents

EGMONT

We bring stories to life

First published in Great Britain 2012 by Egmont UK Limited
239 Kensington High Street, London W8 6SA

Activities and story adaptations by Brenda Apsley.
Edited by Catherine Shoolbred.
Designed by Catherine Ellis.

© 2012 Viacom International Inc. All rights reserved.
Nickelodeon, SpongeBob SquarePants and all related titles,
logos and characters are trademarks of Viacom International Inc.
Created by Stephen Hillenburg.

ISBN 978 1 4052 6340 5
51519/2
Printed in Italy

WANTED

SpongeBob SquarePants

Wanted for crimes against making the world a miserable place.

species:	sponge
appearance:	yellow, with lots of pores
eyes:	2, both blue
address:	Pineapple House, 124 Conch Street, Bikini Bottom
family:	father Harold, mother Margaret, pet snail Gary
occupation:	fry cook at the Krusty Krab
likes:	his job, jellyfishing, Sandy Cheeks
dislikes:	nothing, really
ambition:	1. To be Employee of the Month 2. To pass his boating test
likely to say:	What a fantabulastical day!

Check out these mugshots. Which shows the real SpongeBob?

a  b  c  d

Answer on page 68.

WANTED

Patrick Star

Wanted for crimes against doing stuff ... any stuff.

species: starfish

appearance: pink, smooth as a baby's you-know-what

eyes: 2 (often closed)

address: Rock, 120 Conch Street, Bikini Bottom

family: Parents Herb and Margie, and SpongeBob feels like family, too

occupation: sleeping, lazing around, eating

likes: his best friend, SpongeBob

dislikes: alarm clocks

ambition: to sleep, laze around and eat

likely to say: It's gonna rock!

Add ticks by the things Patrick likes to eat.

a b c d e f g h

Answers on page 68.

9

WANTED

Sandy Cheeks

Wanted for crimes against safe sports.

species:	squirrel
appearance:	brown fur, bushy tail, wears an air dome helmet and spacesuit
eyes:	2, black
address:	TreeDome, Bikini Bottom
family:	Ma and Pa Cheeks and her twin brother Randy
occupation:	scientist
likes:	karate, weight lifting, surfing, boarding
dislikes:	wimps and loafing around
ambition:	to be ka-rah-tay queen of the seas!
likely to say:	Yee-ha! (she's from Texas)

WANTED

Squidward Tentacles

Wanted for crimes against being happy.

species:	octopus
appearance:	grey with a big nose, bald head, tentacle arms and legs
eyes:	2, brown
address:	Tiki Head House, 122 Conch Street, Bikini Bottom
family:	a father (who's just like him)
occupation:	cashier at the Krusty Krab
likes:	latte coffees and playing the clarinet
dislikes:	his job, his life, everything and everyone
ambition:	to have a top-selling record with the Bikini Bottom Philharmonic Orchestra
likely to say:	Go away!

WANTED

Mr Eugene R. Krabs

Wanted for crimes against spending money.

species:	crab
appearance:	red, big claws
eyes:	2, on stalks
address:	Anchor house, Bikini Bottom
family:	mother Betsy, late father Victor and his whale of a daughter, Pearl
occupation:	owner of the Krusty Krab
likes:	money (making it, saving it, counting it, kissing it)
dislikes:	spending money
ambition:	to be the richest crab in the world
likely to say:	Money! Money Money! I ♥ money!

WANTED

Sheldon Plankton

Wanted for crimes against food.

species:	plankton
appearance:	small, green with 2 antennae
eyes:	1, red
address:	The Chum Bucket, Bikini Bottom
family:	his computer wife Karen
occupation:	owner of the Chum Bucket
likes:	plotting and scheming
dislikes:	anyone who knows the Krabby Patty secret ingredient!
likely to say:	Noooooo! (when his plan to steal the Krabby Patty recipe is foiled AGAIN!)

WANTED: YOU!

Add all YOUR details below:

Wanted for crimes against ....

species: ....

appearance: ....

eyes: ....

address: ....

family: ....

occupation: ....

likes: ....

dislikes: ....

ambition: ....

likely to say: ....

What would you be called if you lived in Bikini Bottom? Maybe Elvis Eel, C.C. Slug or Barnacle Boy? Make up a name and address for you there!

My Bikini Bottom name:

....

....

My Bikini Bottom address:

....

....

Plankton is a minuscule master of disguise. Can you find two pictures that match?

a   b   c   d   e

Answer on page 68.

SpongeDoku

Can you do-do-do this **SpongeDoku** puzzle?
Write in the missing numbers from 1 to 6 so ...

- All 6 numbers appear once in each row across →
- All 6 numbers appear once in each row down ↓
- All 6 numbers appear once in each set of 6 boxes

Tip: Use a pencil so you can erase any boo-boos!

3		1			4
	4	6	1	2	3
1			4		6
		4		1	
6				4	1
4	1	5		3	

Why was the snake good at sums?
Because it was an adder!

13

Mr Krabs Takes a Vacation

One day, Mr Krabs had some dramatic news for his employees. **Dum, dum, dummmm ...** **"As of tomorrow,"** he told them, **"I'm CLOSING the Krusty Krab!"**

"HAL-LE-LUUU-YAH!" squealed Squidward. He really HATED his job!

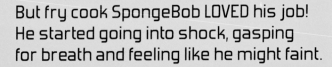

But fry cook SpongeBob LOVED his job! He started going into shock, gasping for breath and feeling like he might faint.

"Relax, boy," said Mr Krabs, slapping him on the shoulder. **"I'm just going on VACATION!"**

SpongeBob drew a huge breath of relief.

Pearl was going too, and SpongeBob was allowed to join them after he agreed to **pay**. Mr Krabs never does miss a money-making opportunity!

Soon they were on their way, but where on earth **(or under the sea)** were they going?

"**Super Mega Mall World?**" squealed Pearl as she spotted it.

"**No, no, the place we're going to is much better,**" said Mr Krabs firmly.

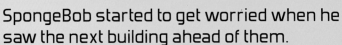

A little later, Pearl gasped as she spotted another sign: "**We're going to Planet Rollercoaster!**" she yelled. But Mr Krabs drove straight past it.

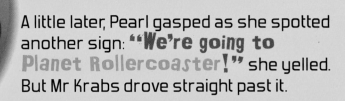

SpongeBob started to get worried when he saw the next building ahead of them. "**The TEENAGE BOY MUSEUM!**" Pearl screamed at supersonic level. But Mr Krabs didn't stop there either **(thank goodness)!**

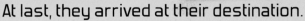

At last, they arrived at their destination. "**It's the Bikini Bottom Mint, where they make all the MONEY,**" said Mr Krabs. "**Have you ever seen anything more beautiful in all your life?**"

Unsurprisingly, no one was quite as excited about it as Mr Krabs!

Inside the Mint, Bill, the ironically-named tour guide, showed the visitors where the money was made.

Mr Krabs was having trouble breathing, seeing all that money. **"Hooaa … hoooaa … hoooaa …"** he squeaked excitedly.

"Sir! Get a hold of yourself! It's just paper!" said SpongeBob.

"Just PAPER?" said Mr Krabs in amazement. **"That's like saying the ocean's just water. Or the Krabby Patty is just a sandwich!"**

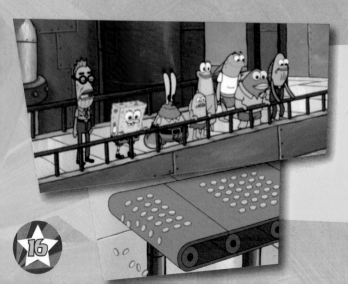

"Ahem!" said Bill, who didn't appreciate their noisy interruptions. He led everyone to see where the coins were **"collected in batches of one million pieces."**
"Wuh … one million!" yelped Mr Krabs, feeling hypnotised by the shiny silver coins.

Sighing quietly in frustration, Bill lead them to the next stage of the tour. **"This machine is where we destroy old money,"** Bill told them.

"DESTROY MONEY? NOOOOOOO!" weeped Mr Krabs. That was **the worst** thing he had ever heard!

"Mr Krabs, it's OK," said SpongeBob, seeing his boss curled up in a ball. **"The shredded money is turned into brand NEW money ... see?"**

Mr Krabs did see. He leapt to his feet and shouted: **"It's a miracle!"**

By now, Bill the normally mild-mannered tour guide had had enough. **"Guards! Get these good-for-nothing dawdlers out!"** he yelled.

But the guards had their own problems. They had been tied up by **criminals** who were busy stuffing money into sacks!

But the criminals hadn't **banked** on Mr Krabs. There was **NO WAY** he was going to let them take away the lovely money!

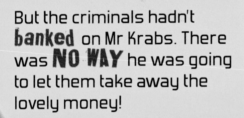

Mr Krabs tackled the robbers using SpongeBob as his weapon. He tied them up with spongy yellow rope **(guess who!)** then hurled them into the back of a passing police car. **Job done!**

"Good work, boy," said Mr Krabs.
"You too, Sir," smiled SpongeBob.

Bill and the tour party burst into applause. Mr Krabs and SpongeBob were their heroes! **"Clearly I misjudged you,"** said Bill. **"On behalf of the Mint I would like to present you with limited edition dollar bills with your faces on them!"**

"Wow, they're ..." said SpongeBob, who was about to take his reward.

"... MINE!" said Mr Krabs, snatching SpongeBob's prize as well as his own. **"I haven't charged ya yet for taggin' along on my vacation!"**

The End

Mint Maze

Which route do you need to take to pass all three places Pearl wanted to visit before reaching the Mint? Watch out for the robbers though, they're still after the money!

SUPER MEGA MALL WORLD

TEENAGE BOY MUSEUM

PLANET ROLLERCOASTER

How many dollar bills did you spot in the maze? Count them up before Mr Krabs (or the robbers) grab them all!

THE MINT

Answer on page 68.

Bill's Bills

Mr Krabs and SpongeBob loved the limited edition dollar bills they were given for foiling the Mint robbery. Complete their prize by drawing the heroic duo in the white circles.

Answers on page 68.

Colour in all the coins with Pearl on them. How many are there? Are there enough for Pearl to pay the $15 entrance fee to the Teenage Boy Museum?

21

Stars of the Sea

Think you know all about the oddball creatures in the sea? You're wrong! Come meet and greet these amazing creatures of the deep!

SpongeBob SquarePants is a part of the worldwide **sponge** family, who are among the simplest of all animals (big surprise!) All sponges have pores, water channels and two layers of cells separated by a jelly-like layer – yuck!

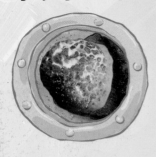 

Talking of jelly . . . did you know that **jellyfish** don't have brains and are 95% water? So they're very dumb and very wet! The Arctic Giant Jellyfish has 36-metre-long tentacles — yowsers!

Larry the Lobster is the muscle-bound lifeguard of Mussel Beach. Like his **lobster** relatives, he has one blunt claw to crush things and one with sharp 'teeth' to cut things. Pretty useful if he needs to do any D.I.Y! His relatives can live for up to 70 years. Live long and prosper, lobsters!

Mr Krabs only eats Krabby Patties, but his **crab** relatives will eat almost anything. They can be small enough to live in mussel shells or absolutely huge like the Japanese Spider Crab, whose legs can grow up to 3 metres long! Tiny Hermit Crabs live in abandoned shells, discarded drinks cans or even paint pots!

Patrick Starfish doesn't look like his **starfish** relatives who all have 5 arms but no head. Starfish don't have brains, which explains a lot about Patrick! They can grow from 8cm to 1 metre wide and live for around 6 years. They can also grow new arms if they break or if they are bitten off, which is a pretty neat trick!

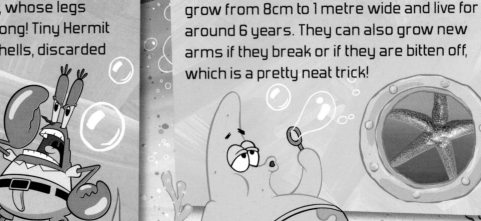

What you need to do:

1 Trace, photocopy or copy the mask onto card.

2 Cut around the dotted lines to cut out the mask.

3 Add a happy, sad or crazy expression on the mask, then colour it in.

4 Ask an adult to cut out the pupils to make eyeholes.

5 Ask an adult to cut out a strip of card measuring 5cm by 30cm. Put it around your head and use tape to join the ends together to make a headband.

6 Tape it to the back of the mask but don't cover the eyeholes! Now your mask is ready to wear!

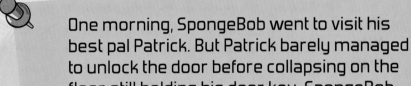

Patrick's Staycation

One morning, SpongeBob went to visit his best pal Patrick. But Patrick barely managed to unlock the door before collapsing on the floor still holding his door key. SpongeBob was **shocked**. Patrick looked a **wreck**!

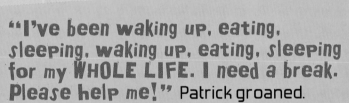

"What have you done to yourself?" SpongeBob asked, as Patrick lay on the floor moaning.

"I've been waking up, eating, sleeping, waking up, eating, sleeping for my WHOLE LIFE. I need a break. Please help me!" Patrick groaned.

SpongeBob smiled as an idea came to him. **"Pal, what you need is a VACATION!"** he told Patrick.

But vacations were costly and Patrick was broke so ...

"You can take a STAY-cation!" smiled SpongeBob. "Take your vacation AT HOME. No packing, no travel, best of all ... it's FREE!"

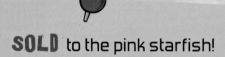 SOLD to the pink starfish!

Seconds later, SpongeBob became hotel receptionist Todd. He welcomed **VIP guest** Mr Star to the Star Rock Inn.

But Patrick's staycation didn't get off to a great start ...

He didn't like his hotel room (which was too much like his own room, them being one and the same!) Bellboy SpongeBob spent an hour rearraning it only for Patrick to decide it had been better the way it was before! Aaarrgggghhh!

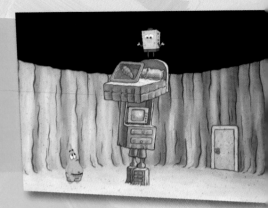

Lifeguard SpongeBob tried to tempt his guest with the relaxing qualities of the bathtub pool, but Patrick quickly got cold and hungry. "One Krabby Patty coming up!" called Chef SpongeBob from the barbecue.

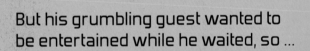

But his grumbling guest wanted to be entertained while he waited, so ...

... Chef SpongeBob became the all-singing, all-dancing SpongeBob Follies!

Mr Star was not impressed. His verdict? "Boring!"

Find the Fizz

Patrick's favourite food is Cheese Fizz! He likes to keep some in his back pocket, but it's gone missing! Can you find **CHEESE** and **FIZZ** in this grid? Quick, get on the case before Patrick floods the page with drool!

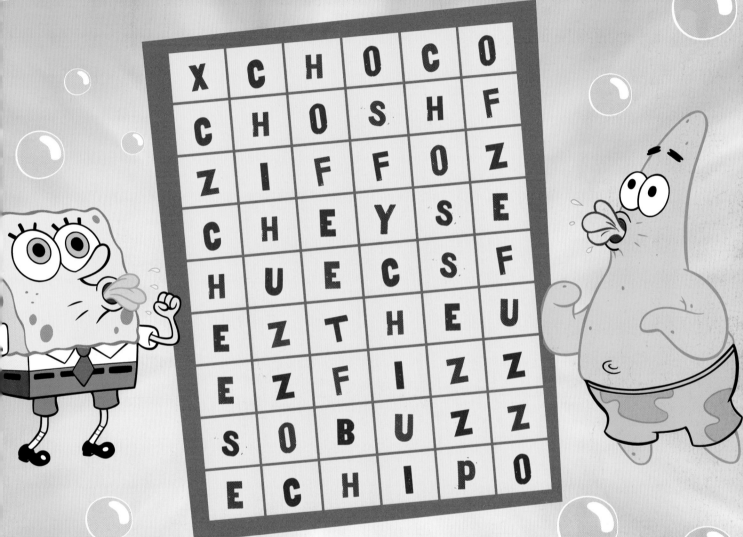

The one thing **Patrick loves** almost as much as Cheese Fizz, is blowing bubbles and popping them! **Count up** all the bubbles, then **circle** the matching number.

22   **25**   **30**   **31**   **33**

Peddlin' Pals

SpongeBob, Patrick and Mr Krabs are best biking buddies! These pictures look the same, but can you spot 10 differences in picture b?

Answers on page 68.

Ka-rah-tay!

Draw in what's missing in these pictures of Sandy Cheeks so all 4 are the same.

I'm hotter than a hickory-smoked sausage!

it's Magic!

SpongeBob and Patrick love being in the spotlight. You too can be a star, when you perform this **amazing MAGIC trick!**

What you need:
- **12 playing cards**
- **safety scissors**
- **non-toxic glue**

Use safety scissors and get adult help to learn this trick before amazing your family and friends!

1

Use safety scissors to make a 3-sided cut in one of the cards to make a little flap as shown.

2

Put glue on the back of another card and stick it to the picture side of the card with the flap, so the two cards look like one card, but **don't stick down the flap!** Then leave it to dry.

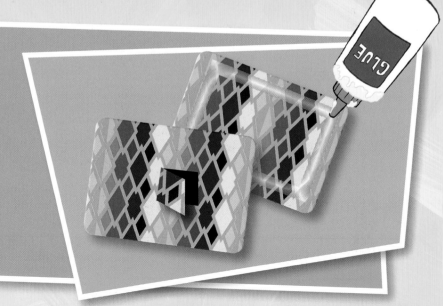

3

Prepare your trick!
Hold the flap between your second and third fingers, so it can't be seen. Slide up to 10 playing cards between the trick card and your hand.

4

Perform the trick!
Keep your hand and the cards flat on a table and tell your audience that you will lift all the cards using your **magnetic powers!** Say a magic word like **alakazam!** then slowly lift your hand. All the cards will lift off the table as if by **magic!**

What happened when the magician got mad?

He pulled his hare out!

Wow! How'd he do that?

A SquarePants Family Vacation

Do all the voice and actions so **YOU** can be the star of this story!

- When you see a picture, say their name.
- When you come to 3 words in brackets (–/–/–), cross out 2 words, leaving 1 word to keep in your story.
- When you come to a blank line, add a word of your choice!
- Characters:

SpongeBob Larry Squidward Sandy Mr Krabs Mrs Puff Plankton the monster Patrick

A star is born!

 sent cards to his friends, inviting them to a special evening.

"A free (honey/ money/ bunny) **party? This sounds too good to be true!**" said .

"A (latte/ nappy/ patty)-sipping contest? This sounds too, too good to be true!" said .

"A science (bear/ fair/ pear)! **This sounds plum too good to be _____!**" said .

"A (plate/ gate/ weight)-lifting competition? **That sounds too good to be true!**" said .

"A quiet evening studying the rules of the (toad/ road/ load)? That sounds _____ good to be true!" said .

"A meeting about the ultimate downfall of the (musty lab/ Krusty Krab/ rusty cab)? **That sounds too good to be true!**" said .

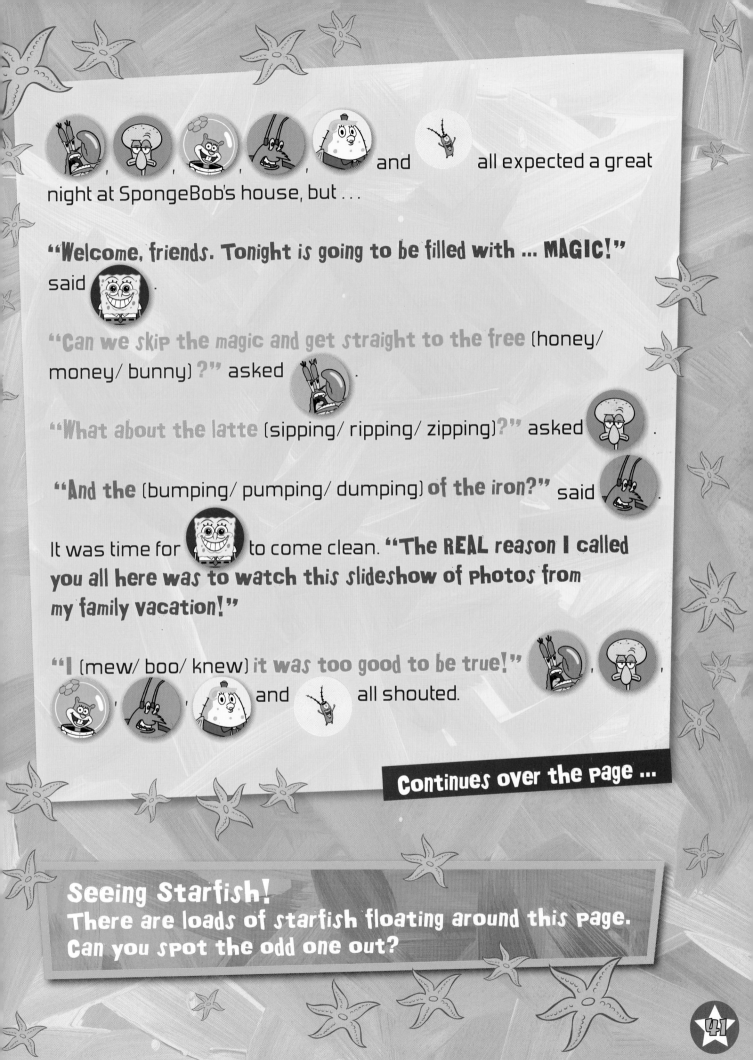

, , , , and all expected a great night at SpongeBob's house, but …

"Welcome, friends. **Tonight** is going to be filled with … **MAGIC!**" said .

"Can we skip the magic and get straight to the free (honey/ money/ bunny)?" asked .

"What about the latte (sipping/ ripping/ zipping)?" asked .

"And the (bumping/ pumping/ dumping) of the iron?" said .

It was time for to come clean. "The REAL reason I called you all here was to watch this slideshow of photos from my family vacation!"

"I (mew/ boo/ knew) it was too good to be true!" , , and all shouted.

Continues over the page …

Seeing Starfish!
There are loads of starfish floating around this page.
Can you spot the odd one out?

The **boat crash**, the **trip into space**, the breakdown ... the slideshow went ON and ON, until got the part where he and hurtled down a mega-slide and heard a sound. A **SCARY** sound. Now they had everyone's attention, they told them all about it ...

"G–r–o–w–l!" said , but thought it was Patrick.

"**Are you getting** (mad/ hungry/ tired)**?**" asked .

"Yeah I am!" replied . ."How'd you know?"

"**I could hear your** (brain/ stomach/ knee) **growling. I thought it might be some kinda SCAARY MONSTER coming to** (beat/ eat/ greet) **us!**" said .

"Ha, ha, ha," laughed .

"**Ha, ha, ha,**" laughed .

"G–r–r–o–o–w–l!" said again.

"**That's funny. Couldn't have been my stomach growling, though. I had its** (vocal cords/ ears/ nose) **removed before the trip!**" said .

"G–r–r–r–o–w–w–w–l!" said , even closer this time.

"(Run/ sun/ bun) **for your** (wife/ knife/ life)**!**" yelled .

"G-r-r-r-o-o-o-w-w-w-l-l-l!" said right behind them.

"WAAAAAAAHHHHHHHHH!" said .

"I saw this in a movie once!" said .

"OK, now what?" asked .

"I'm not sure – I fell asleep."

SpongeBob and Patrick ran away faster than they had ever run away in their entire lives!

"Hooray for not being eaten!" said . But all this 'not being eaten' is making me hungry!"

The End

AHHHHH!

AHHHHH!

Draw the monster here and give it a scary name!

The Making of a Fry Cook

Fill in the labels to show what makes the ultimate fry cook.

Why is SpongeBob the best cook? He's CHEAP!

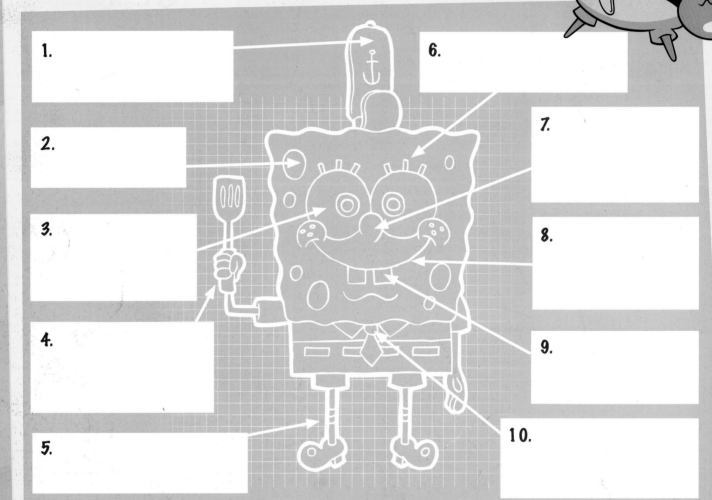

1.

2.

3.

4.

5.

6.

7.

8.

9.

10.

- Fry cook hat
- Pore
- Patty-flipping mechanism holder
- Lower leg warmer
- Eyelashes

- Burning patty warning system
- Window to innards
- Frown turned upside down
- Perfectly executed knot
- Smile reflectors

What does Patrick say to the Krabby Patty? Pleased to EAT you!

Krabby Patty DNA

At last, here's the blueprint for the perfect Krabby Patty!
Write in the labels to show where all the yummy bits go.

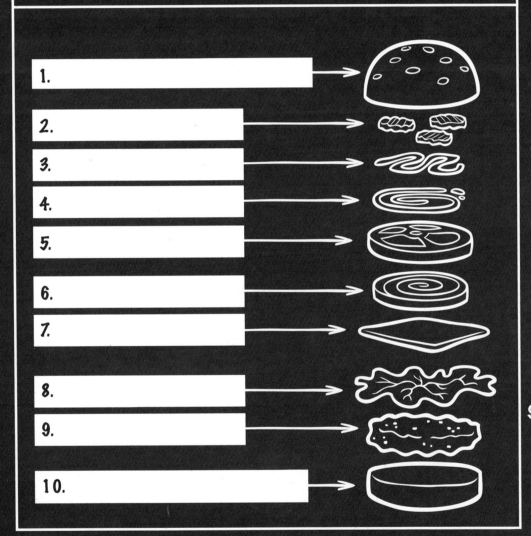

KRABBY PATTY DNA

1.
2.
3.
4.
5.
6.
7.
8.
9.
10.

Ingredients List

Sea Lettuce

Undersea Cheese

Sea Pickles

Sea Onion

Seaweed Seed Bun Top

Maritime Mustard

Sea Tomato

Krabby Patty

Seaweed Seed Bun Bottom

Krusty Ketchup

One thing is missing, the **secret ingredient!** Draw
what you think it is here, but DON'T tell Plankton!

Oh, no! Plankton is hiding out in the hope of discovering
the **secret ingredient**. Can you spot him?

To the JellyFish Fields!

Wow! There's been a sighting of the rare green jellyfish in the Jellyfish Fields! It's super-lucky, so SpongeBob and Patrick want to catch it! Play the game with friends.

What you need:
- a coin
- a counter for each player (buttons can be used). **No, not belly buttons!**

How to play:
- Put your counters on the START.
- Take turns to flip the coin. Move on 1 space if it lands head side up, or 2 spaces if it lands tail side up.
- If you land on a **Pink Jellyfish**, you get stung! Say, "OUCH!" really loudly, then go back 3 spaces.
- If you land on a **Guard Fish**, say, "EEK!" and miss a turn.
- If you land on **The Flying Scotsman** go all the way back to the START!
- The first player to reach the **Rare Green Jellyfish** gets a cheer from the other players because **they've WON!**

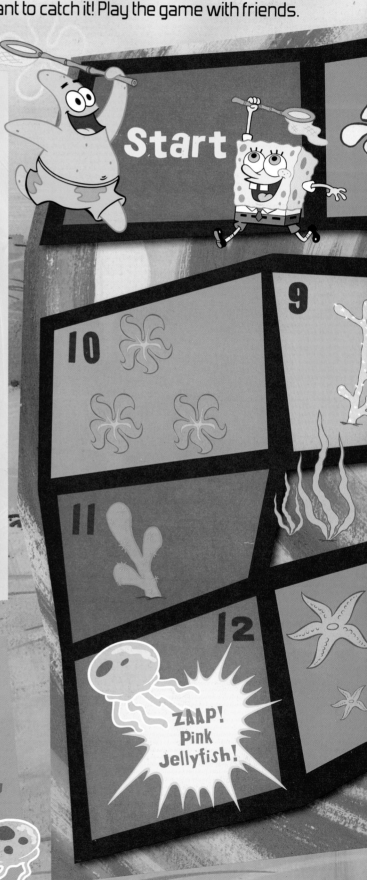

Start

10

9

11

12

ZAAP! Pink Jellyfish!

What did Gary say when he met a stinging jellyfish?

"mi-OW!"

Mooncation

One morning, Sandy Cheeks was getting her rocket ready for take off, when her square spongy pal came to see her.

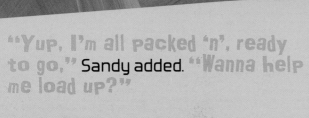

"**Where ya going?**" asked SpongeBob.
"**The MOOOOON!**" said Sandy.

"Yup, I'm all packed 'n', ready to go," Sandy added. "Wanna help me load up?"

But SpongeBob had raced away.

Sandy climbed aboard her rocket before SpongeBob raced back carrying a '**Have fun on the moon see you soon**' cake!

But Sandy had already started the launch countdown: T-minus twelve ... eleven ... ten ... nine ... eight ... seven ... six ... five ...

"WAIT!" yelled SpongeBob. "You can't go without your caaaaaaake!"

But the countdown continued: ... four ... three ... two ... one. LAUNCH COMMENCING! SpongeBob grabbed the ladder and hurled himself inside the rocket.

"Looks like you're going on a mooncation!" Sandy told him.

Then she saw the cake. "You can't bring regular food into space," she said. "It will float off in all directions!"

Which it did.

"Aw, nuts!" said Sandy, as the cake split into bits and floated all around them. SPLAT!

49

Soon, the intrepid space travellers landed on the moon. Sandy got out two boards so they could do some **moon crater boarding**!

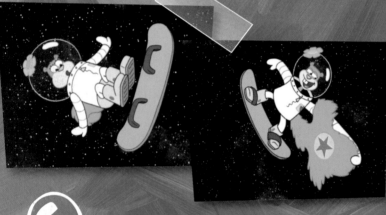

"Here's the Flippity Doo Dah and this is the Texas Tail Crab!" she yelled, as she twisted and turned in zero gravity.

But when **Spaceboy SpongeBob** had a turn, he just floated up into space.

"Uh, oh! SpongeBob's too light in the lunar gravity," thought Sandy.

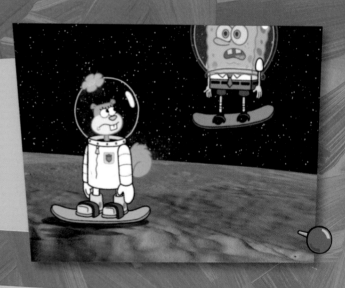

Sandy's solution? SpongeBob should **rock out**! With a heavy rock on his helmet, SpongeBob could **moonboard** like a pro!

"Watch this!" he squealed as he spun around. "A no-look one-footed tongue-out ..."

"... smash into the side of the rocket!" THUMP!

"You should call it the 'no-look one-footed tongue-out puncture the fuel tank'!" said Sandy, as the fuel tank started emptying. OOPS!

"C'mon!" yelled Sandy. "We gotta go while there's still enough fuel to make it home."

"We've lost control. We're coming in too steep!" Sandy yelled as they headed for home.

"Is that bad?" asked SpongeBob.

"Only if you consider being consumed by a giant fireball "bad"," said Sandy, as she headed outside.

Things did not look good. GULP!

Sandy lassoed the rocket's nose cone and pulled back hard. **"Yip, yip, YIPPEY! YEEHAW!"**

The **super-strong scientist squirrel's** plan worked! After a bumpy landing, Sandy got them safely back to Bikini Bottom. **PHEW!**

Former **Spaceboy SpongeBob** felt really bad. **"Oh, Sandy, I'm so sorry I ruined your mooncation,"** he wailed.

"Ruined?" said Sandy in surprise. **"Heck, NO! That was the most fun I've had in a toad's age. Soon as I fix mah rocket, you and me is heading to ... MARS!"**

The End

We're All Goin' ... on a Road Trip!

Which 3 pieces complete the puzzle? Draw and colour them in.

 a

 b

 c

 d

e

 f

Can you see where is the bus above is going? Write the name on this sign, then draw a picture of who they might see there.

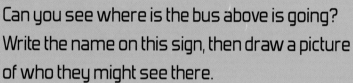

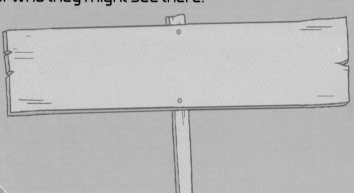

Everyone wanted to go on the Road Trip, but two of them missed the bus. Can you identify them from their shapes?

What does Gary use to keep his shell shiny? SNAIL POLISH!

SpongeBob SquareLaughs

Zzzzzzz. Patrick's had a long day. He's been up since the crack of yawn!

Why does Patrick want his name written on his arm? So he won't forget who he is!

Patrick is sooooo lazy. The only exercise he gets is stretching his mouth when he yawns!

What do you get if you cross a pig with a cactus?

A porkerpine!

There are two fish in a tank. One says to the other, "Do you know how to drive this thing?"

What do bees like to chew?

Bumble gum!

What lies at the bottom of the ocean and shakes?

A nervous wreck!

DoodleBob

Take a l-o-n-g look at this doodle-fest, then tick (✓) the doodles you can see and add a cross (✗) by the ones that you can't.

1. ☐ 2. ☐ 3. ☐ 4. ☐ 5. ☐

6. ☐ 7. ☐ 8. ☐ 9. ☐ 10. ☐

11. ☐ 12. ☐ 13. ☐

14. ☐ 15. ☐

16. ☐

True or false?

1. The ice lolly is yellow. ☐
2. There are 3 red shells. ☐
3. The camera is red. ☐

Answers on page 68.

56

Doodle your **favourite friend** from Bikini Bottom below.
Don't forget to add your DoodleName too!

My Doodle by Doodler ....

Spread the joy!

Yee-haaaaa!

Friends make everything friendlier!

As long as these pants are square and this sponge is Bob, I will not let you down!

The Krabby Patty Game

Have fun making Krabby Patties and use them to play a fantabulastical game!

You will need:

- thin card
- glue and safety scissors
- red, green and brown felt-tip pens
- optional extra: 12 copper and 12 silver-coloured coins

get adult help

use safety scissors

What you need to do:

1 Photocopy or draw 24 Krabby Patty shapes (like this one) ▶ Glue them onto thin card. (Or, get 12 copper-coloured coins and 12 silver-coloured coins to use instead of the Krabby Patty cards).

2 Use felt-tip pens to colour in the Krabby Patties. Add a green dot on 12 of them and a red dot on the other 12. Then ask an adult to cut them out.

How to play:

- Each player plays with either the red or green dotted Krabby Patties or the copper or silver-coloured coins.

- Take turns to place a Krabby Patty (or coin) on the grid opposite.

- The winner is the first to place 3 of their Krabby Patties (or coins) in a row across, up, down, or diagonally. To make things harder, see if you can get 4 Krabby Patties in a row!

Krabby Patty Snap!

- Shuffle both sets of cards and place them picture-side-down on a flat surface.

- Take turns to turn over 2 cards. If you find a pair of red or green dotted ones you win the cards and have an extra turn. Keep playing until you've found all the pairs.

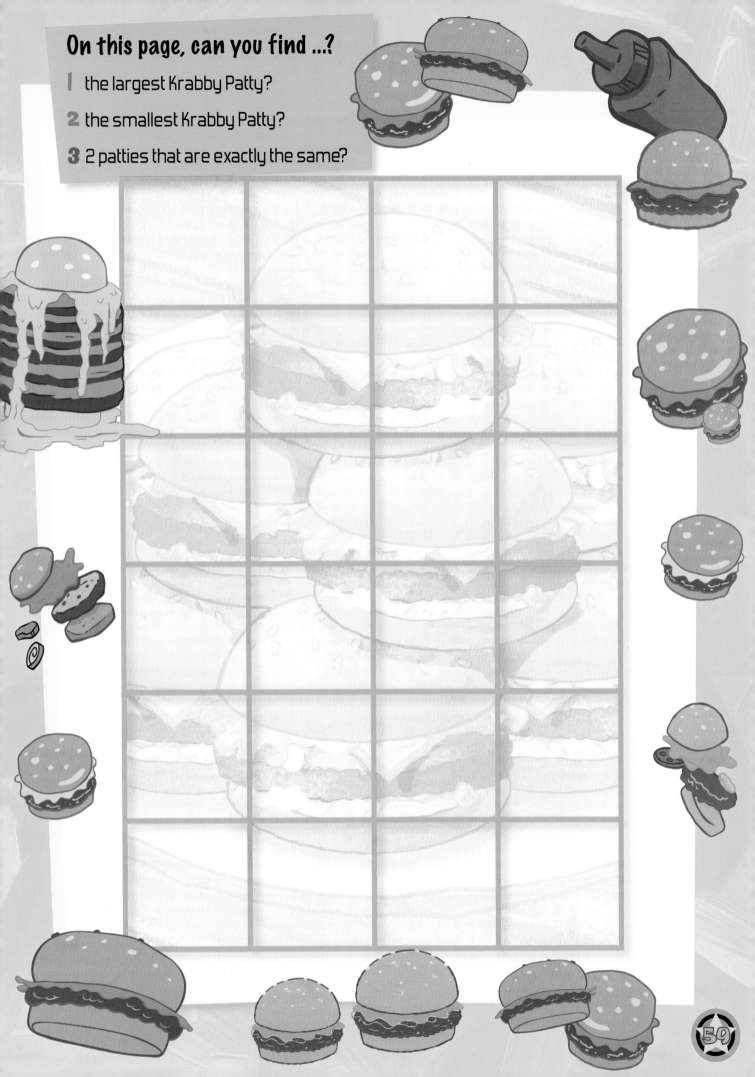

On this page, can you find ...?

1 the largest Krabby Patty?

2 the smallest Krabby Patty?

3 2 patties that are exactly the same?

Walking the Plankton

One day, penny-pinching Mr Krabs got his pincers on two **FREE** tickets for a relaxing cruise ship holiday!

"**I'm leavin' you in charge,**" he told SpongeBob. "**See ya when I see ya!**"

But SpongeBob saw the tickets were for '**you and a guest**'. He had an idea of what the perfect guest would be: small, square and spongy!

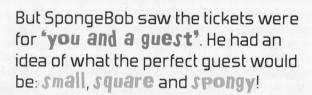

"**I suppose I could make that extra ticket available to whoever wants to be me manservant!**" said Mr Krabs.

"Right this way, Sir!" said super smiley **Manservant SpongeBob**!

But there was just one problem. Would the **Krabby Patty secret recipe** be safe while they were away? Probably not, so ...

"**I'm bringin' the secret formula,**" said Mr Krabs. "**Just in case our absence proves too tempting to a certain one-eyed creepy-crawly!**" who just happened to be listening in!

Plankton bought cruise tickets for him and his computer wife Karen. A **romantic getaway**? Well yes, a second honeymoon as far as Karen was concerned. But Plankton's heart was set on stealing the **Krabby Patty recipe**!

Mr Krabs and **Manservant SpongeBob** enjoyed their cruise, little knowing that **evil mini mastermind** Plankton was on their trail.

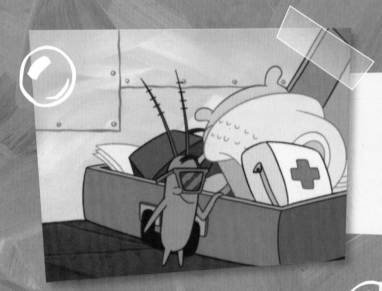

In his quest to steal the **secret recipe**, Plankton had packed some unusual objects for the cruise. **"Suntan lotion, sunglasses ... death laser,"** he muttered to himself.

Mr Krabs took advantage of all the cruise freebies he could get his pincers on! His eyes lit up when he saw a buffet stand. **"Ooh! FREE FOOD!"** he said.

But then he tasted it. **"BLEUGH!"** he gasped. **"That tastes like putrefied coral stems dipped in rotten butter sauce!"**

He spat it out saying, **"How can anyone STAND this slop? Makes me miss our grub at the Krusty Krab."**

Then he had a **money-making idea**! **"SpongeBob, be a good manservant and fix me up a Krabby Patty, would ya?"** he said.

SpongeBob fetched his portable grill. **"A good fry cook is never far from his grill,"** he smiled.

Before long, the **Krabby Patty smell** had attracted a crowd of hungry passengers. **"Order up, Mister Krabs!"** announced SpongeBob, as he finished cooking.

"**Looks like we got a business venture on our hands,**" said Mr Krabs. "**Krabby Patties! Come an' get yer Krabby Patties!**" he announced, rubbling his pincers together in glee.

Plankton, in disguise, was first in the queue. "**Watch me sucker this guy,**" Mr Krabs whispered to SpongeBob. "**That'll be a mere one hundred dollars!**" he told the small moustached man.

"**That's all? Heh, heh, hee,**" said the tiny stranger, handing over the money.

But the money smelled awful! "**Wayduhminut!**" yelled Mr Krabs. "**There's CHUM all over this bill! Where'd ya get this?**" he demanded.

"**From the same place this is goin',**"said Plankton, grabbing the Krabby Patty and flying away, "**the Chum Bucket laboratory! Nice doin' business, Krabs!**"

"NOOOOO!" yelped Mr Krabs, in horror.

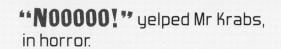

But Plankton's getaway came to a swift halt when he crashed into his wife Karen. **SPLAT!** She was **NOT PLEASED** to discover that her second honeymoon was really another one of Plankton's *patty-grabbing schemes*!

"I KNEW you were up to something!" she sobbed, as she sliced the whole cruise ship in half!

As SpongeBob, Mr Krabs and the **secret recipe** were rescued along with the other passengers, Karen and Plankton sailed off alone. There was **NO WAY** Plankton was going to get out of his second honeymoon!

The End

Ready For Class?

It's time for SpongeBob and Patrick to head back to Poseidon Elementary School and take the **Start of Year Test**!

Take the test then check the answers on page 68. Give yourself **1 point** for each correct answer, then write your total in the red box.

1 In the story **Mooncation**, which planet does Sandy plan to visit next?

- a Venus
- b Mars
- c Pluto

2 Who is related to Mr Krabs?

a

b

c

3 In the story **Walking the Plankton**, what does Mr Krabs smell on the money Plankton hands him?

- a Cheese Fizz
- b Kelp mousse
- c Chum

4 Way to go! Which **shadow** matches these gorgeous cheerleaders?

a ☐

b ☐

c ☐

5 In the story **Patrick's Staycation**, what is the name of the hotel he visits?

☐ **a** Don't Come Inn

☐ **b** Star Rock Inn

☐ **c** Inn Big Trouble

6 **Yuk!** Can you tell which Bikini Bottomers are covered in sticky-icky pink gum here?

Total Score: ☐

5-6 Top of the class!

3-4 Must try harder!

1-2 No comment!

Answers on page 68.

Answers

P8 WANTED: SpongeBob SquarePants
Picture c shows the real SpongeBob.

P9 WANTED: Patrick Star
Patrick eats them all, even the socks and underpants!

P12 WANTED: YOU!
Pictures a and d match.

P13 SpongeDoku

3	2	1	6	5	4
5	4	6	1	2	3
1	5	3	4	6	2
2	6	4	3	1	5
6	3	2	5	4	1
4	1	5	2	3	6

P20 Mint Maze
There are 9 dollar bills in the maze.

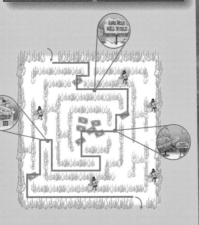

P21 Bill's Bills
There are 14 coins with Pearl on, so Pearl does not have enough for a ticket to the Teenage Boy Museum.

P23 Stars of the Sea
The real creature is b, sea potato.

P24 Mr Krabs' Photo Album
Photo f of Pearl is different. Photos d and f of SpongeBob are the same. There are 23 Squidward photos.

P34 Packing with Patrick
Plankton is in the camera lens.

P35 Find the Fizz
33 bubbles. Ah, didn't you realise? Patrick has already popped 2!

X	C	H	O	C	O
C	H	O	S	H	F
Z	I	F	F	O	Z
C	H	E	Y	S	E
H	U	E	C	S	F
E	Z	T	H	E	U
E	Z	F	I	Z	Z
S	O	B	U	Z	Z
E	C	H	I	P	O

P36 Peddlin' Pals

P37 Ka-rah-tay!
a - helmet, b - acorn, c - red dots and d - stripes

P41 Seeing Starfish
The odd starfish is on the right of the page. It has 7 arms.

P44 The Making of a Fry Cook

1. Fry Cook Hat
2. Pore
3. Window to innards
4. Patty-flipping Mechanism Holder
5. Lower Leg Warmer
6. Eyelashes
7. Burning Patty Warning System
8. Frown Turned Upside Down
9. Smile Reflectors
10. Perfectly Executed Knot

P45 Krabby Patty DNA
1 Seaweed Seed Bun Top, 2 Sea Pickles, 3 Maritime Mustard 4 Krusty Ketchup, 5 Sea Tomato, 6 Sea Onion, 7 Undersea Cheese, 8 Sea Lettuce, 9 Krabby Patty, 10 Seaweed Seed Bun Bottom. Plankton is by the title.

P54 We're All Goin' ... on a Road Trip!
Pieces a, d and f complete the jigsaw. The bus is going to ATLANTIS. Plankton and Gary missed the bus.

P56 DoodleBob
1-✓, 2-✗, 3-✓, 4-✓, 5-✗, 6-✗, 7-✓, 8-✗, 9-✗, 10-✗, 11-✓, 12-✓, 13-✗, 14-✗, 15-✓, 16-✓.
True or False: 1 – False, the lolly is white, 2 – False, there is only 1, and 3 – True.

P58 The Krabby Patty Game

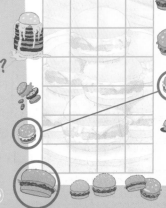

P66 Ready for Class?
1 b – Mars 2 c – Pearl
3 c – Chum 4 shadow c
5 b – Star Rock Inn
6 Squidward, Patrick, SpongeBob and Sandy are covered in goo.